A POCKET FULL OF PIE

a poetry anthology
selected by
Morag Styles

Contents

There Was An Old Lady

There was an old lady
  Whose kitchen was bare,
So she called for the cat
  Saying, "Time for some air!"

She sent him to buy her
  A packet of cheese.
But the cat hurried back
  With a basket of bees.

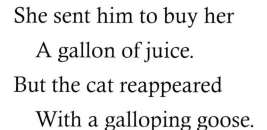

She sent him to buy her
  A gallon of juice.
But the cat reappeared
  With a galloping goose.

She sent him to buy her
  A dinner of beef.
But the cat scampered home
  With an Indian chief.

She sent him to buy her
  A bowl of ice cream.
But the cat skated in
  With a whole hockey team.

She sent him to buy her
  A bite of spaghetti.
But the cat strutted up
  With a bride and confetti.

She sent him to buy her
  A fine cup of tea.
But the cat waddled back
  With a dinosaur's knee.

The fridge was soon bulging,
  And so was the shelf.
So she sent for a hot dog
  And ate it herself.

Dennis Lee

Old Mother Hubbard

Old Mother Hubbard
Went to the cupboard,
To fetch her poor dog a bone;
When she got there
The cupboard was bare
And so the poor dog had a moan.

Michael Rosen

Sing a Song of Sixpence

Sing a song of sixpence,
A pocket full of pie;
Four and twenty blackbirds,
Baked in a sty.

When the sty was opened
The birds began to sing;
Wasn't that a dainty fish,
To set before the king?

The king was in his counting house,
Counting out his tummy;
The queen was in the parlour,
Eating bread and bunny.

The maid was in the garden,
Hanging out her nose,
When down came a blackbird
And pecked off her clothes.

Michael Rosen

No Hickory No Dickory
No Dock

Wasn't me
Wasn't me
said the little mouse
I didn't run up no clock

You could hickory me
You could dickory me
or lock me in a dock

I still say
I didn't run up no clock

Was me who ran under your bed
Was me who bit into your bread
Was me who nibbled your cheese

But please please,
I didn't run up no clock
no hickory
no dickory
no dock.

John Agard

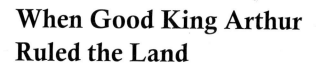

When Good King Arthur Ruled the Land

When good King Arthur ruled the land
He was a goodly king;
He stole three pecks of barley meal
To make a bag-pudding.
A bag-pudding the king did make,
And stuff'd it well with plums;
And in it put great lumps of fat,
As big as my two thumbs.
The king and queen did eat thereof,
And noblemen beside;
And what they could not eat that night,
The queen next morning fried.

Traditional

9

oars draws saws

Playing with Words

You can play with dice
You can play with cards
You can play with a ball
You can play with words

words

words

words

words

words

words

banana

words

words

words

words

words

Michael Rosen

word sword

A Skipping Alphabet

Hey!	bee
sea	dee
eee	
eff	
gee	
aitch	eye
jay	kay
ell	
emm	
enn	
oh!	
pee	
queue	are
ess	tea
you	
vee	

double-you
ex
why?
ZED
and

OUT

Wes Magee

From "The Centipede's Song"

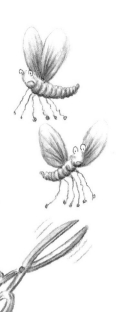

"I've eaten many strange and scrumptious
dishes in my time,
Like jellied gnats and dandyprats and
earwigs cooked in slime,
And mice with rice – they're really nice
When roasted in their prime.
(But don't forget to sprinkle them with
just a pinch of grime.)

"I've eaten fresh mudburgers by the greatest
cooks there are,
And scrambled dregs and stinkbugs' eggs and
hornets stewed in tar,
And pails of snails and lizards' tails,
And beetles by the jar.
(A beetle is improved by just a
splash of vinegar.)

"I often eat boiled slobbages.
They're grand when served beside
Minced doodlebugs and curried slugs.
And have you ever tried
Mosquitoes' toes and wampfish roes
Most delicately fried?
(The only trouble is they disagree
with my inside.)

"I'm mad for crispy wasp-stings on a
piece of buttered toast,
And pickled spines of porcupines.
And then a gorgeous roast
Of dragon's flesh, well hung, not fresh –
It costs a pound at most,
(And comes to you in barrels if you
order it by post.)

"I crave the tasty tentacles of octopi
for tea
I like hot-dogs, I LOVE hot-frogs,
and surely you'll agree
A plate of soil with engine oil's
A super recipe.
(I hardly need to mention that it's
practically free.)"

Roald Dahl

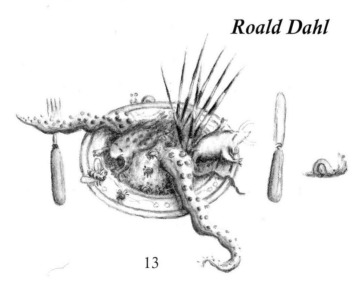

Out in the Desert

Out in the desert lies the sphinx
It never eats and it never drinx
Its body quite solid without any chinx
And when the sky's all purples and pinx
(As if it was painted with coloured inx)
And the sun it ever so swiftly sinx
Behind the hills in a couple of twinx
You may hear (if you're lucky) a bell that clinx
And also tolls and also tinx
And they say at the very same sound the sphinx
It sometimes smiles and it sometimes winx:

But nobody knows just what it thinx.

Charles Causley

Limerick

There was a young lady of Spain
Who was dreadfully sick in the train,
Not once, but again
And again, and again
And again, and again, AND AGAIN.

Anon.

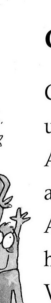

Great Fleas Have Little Fleas

Great fleas have little fleas
upon their backs to bite 'em,
And little fleas have lesser fleas,
and so ad infinitum.
And the great fleas themselves in turn
have greater fleas to go on
While these again have greater still,
and greater still, and so on.

A. De Morgan

Saturday Night

I've tried counting frogs,
I've tried counting dogs,
I've tried counting millions of sheep,
I've counted my toes,
But I can't even doze,
Oh, how can I get to sleep?

My bed's full of bumps,
My pillow's all lumps,
My eiderdown's bunched in a heap,
I've heard a cat yowl
And the screech of an owl,
Oh, how can I get to sleep?

I've thought of a star
Where weary things are,
Like dream-hogs and snorpions that creep,
I've sucked on my thumb
So hard it's gone numb,
Oh, how can I get to sleep?

I've said all the rhymes
I know fifty times,
I'm fed up with Little Bo Peep,
Who cares that Miss Muffet
Sat down on a tuffet?
Oh, how can I get to sleep?

Now what's all that noise:
Chiming bells, yelling boys,
Passing traffic and sparrows going "cheep"?
It's quarter to ten,
Sunday morning again!
Oh, how did I get to sleep?

Richard Edwards

17

Upside-down Cake

I am going to make
An upside-down cake.
I know I'll need some flour,
But I'm going to wait
At least half an hour
Before I begin to bake.

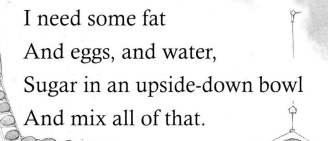

I need some fat
And eggs, and water,
Sugar in an upside-down bowl
And mix all of that.

Before I can really begin
I'll need an upside-down tin,
And an upside-down oven
To fit everything in.

I know you will say
I will have to stand on my head
To eat an upside-down cake.
But I have thought of that:
I will choke and be dead.

So I will change my mind
And bake instead
A sideways cake
And eat it
Sideways in bed.

I. Choonara

The Quangle Wangle's Hat

On the top of the Crumpetty Tree
    The Quangle Wangle sat,
But his face you could not see,
    On account of his Beaver Hat.
For his Hat was a hundred and two feet wide,
With ribbons and bibbons on every side
And bells, and buttons, and loops, and lace,
So that nobody ever could see the face
    Of the Quangle Wangle Quee.

The Quangle Wangle said
    To himself on the Crumpetty Tree, –
"Jam; and jelly; and bread;
    Are the best of food for me!
But the longer I live in this Crumpetty Tree
The plainer than ever it seems to me
That very few people come this way,
And that life on the whole is far from gay!"
    Said the Quangle Wangle Quee.

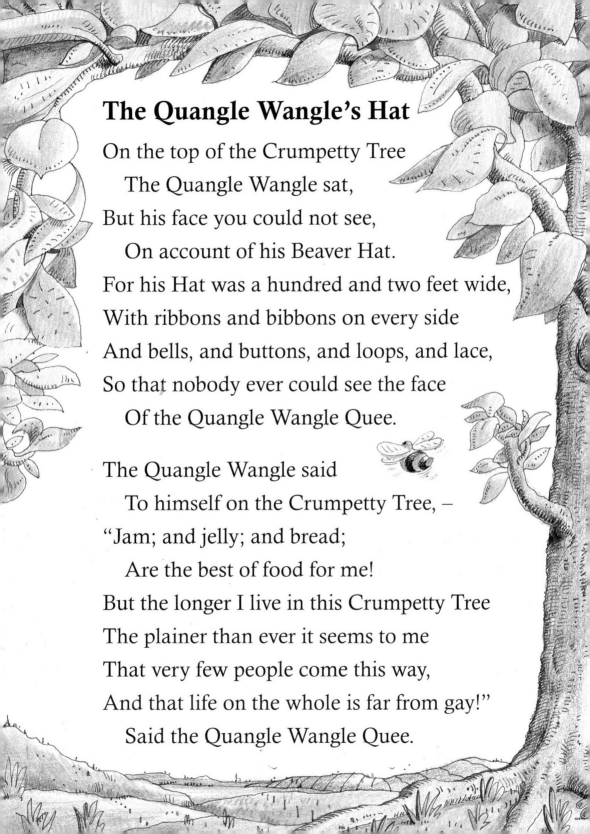

But there came to the Crumpetty Tree,
　　Mr and Mrs Canary;
And they said, – "Did you ever see
　　Any spot so charmingly airy?
May we build a nest on your lovely Hat?
Mr Quangle Wangle, grant us that!
O please let us come and build a nest
Of whatever material suits you best,
　　Mr Quangle Wangle Quee!"

And besides, to the Crumpetty Tree
　　Came the Stork, the Duck, and the Owl;
The Snail and the Bumble-Bee,
　　The Frog, and the Fimble Fowl;
(The Fimble Fowl, with a Corkscrew leg);
And all of them said, – "We humbly beg,
We may build our homes on your lovely Hat, –
Mr Quangle Wangle, grant us that!
　　Mr Quangle Wangle Quee!"

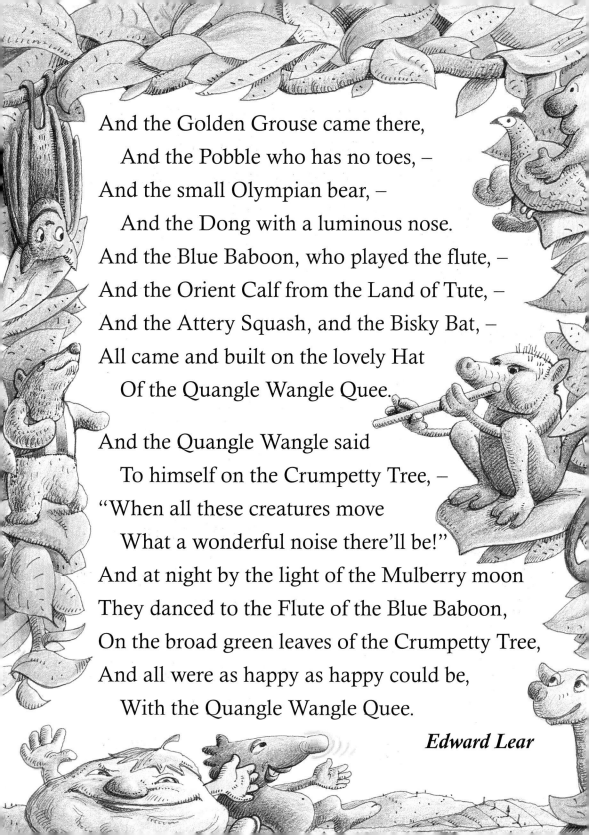

And the Golden Grouse came there,
    And the Pobble who has no toes, –
And the small Olympian bear, –
    And the Dong with a luminous nose.
And the Blue Baboon, who played the flute, –
And the Orient Calf from the Land of Tute, –
And the Attery Squash, and the Bisky Bat, –
All came and built on the lovely Hat
    Of the Quangle Wangle Quee.

And the Quangle Wangle said
    To himself on the Crumpetty Tree, –
"When all these creatures move
    What a wonderful noise there'll be!"
And at night by the light of the Mulberry moon
They danced to the Flute of the Blue Baboon,
On the broad green leaves of the Crumpetty Tree,
And all were as happy as happy could be,
    With the Quangle Wangle Quee.

Edward Lear

Runny Egg

For breakfast I had a runny egg.
I chased it round the table.
It wobbled and it screeched at me,
"Catch me if you are able!"

So I nailed it to the table.

Brian Patten

Acorn Haiku

Just a green olive
In its own little egg-cup:
It can feed the sky.

Kit Wright

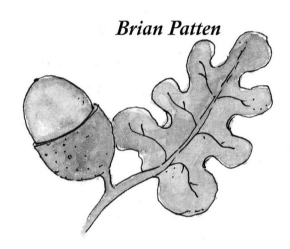

A Clown's Conclusion

We are born. We grow up.
We laugh. We cry.
Then when the egg
inside us stops beating,
it's quite simple. We die.

John Agard

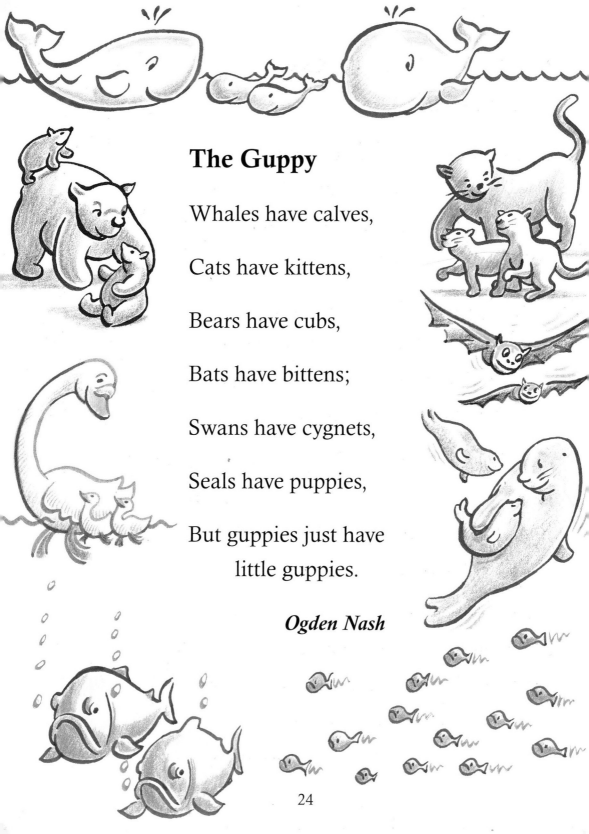

The Guppy

Whales have calves,

Cats have kittens,

Bears have cubs,

Bats have bittens;

Swans have cygnets,

Seals have puppies,

But guppies just have
little guppies.

Ogden Nash

Life's Not Been the Same in my Family

Life's not been the same in my family
since the day that the new baby came,
my parents completely ignore me,
they scarcely remember my name.

The baby gets all their attention,
"Oh, isn't she precious!" they croon,
they think that she looks like an angel,
I think she resembles a prune.

They're thrilled when she giggles or gurgles,
"She burped!" they exclaim with delight,
they don't even mind when she wakes us
with deafening screams in the night.

They seem to believe she's a treasure,
there's simply no way I agree,
I wish she'd stop being a baby
and start being older than me.

Jack Prelutsky

25

New Baby

My baby brother makes so much noise
that the Rottweiler next door
phoned up to complain.

My baby brother makes so much noise
that all the big green frogs
came out of the drains.

My baby brother makes so much noise
that the rats and the mice
wore headphones.

My baby brother makes so much noise
that I can't ask my mum a question,
so much noise that sometimes

I think of sitting the cat on top of him
in his pretty little cot with all his teddies.
But even the cat is terrified of his cries.

So I have devised a plan. A soundproof room.
A telephone to talk to my mum.
A small lift to receive food and toys.

Thing is, it will cost a fortune.
The other thing is, the frogs have gone.
It's not bad now. Not that I like him or anything.

Jackie Kay

Nicely, Nicely

Nicely, nicely, nicely, away in the east,
the rain clouds care for the little corn plants
as a mother cares for her baby.

Native American oral tradition

Night Sounds

When I lie in bed
I think I can hear
The stars being switched on
I think I can.

And I think I can hear
The moon
Breathing.

But I have to be still.
So still.
All the house is sleeping.
Except for me.

Then I think I can hear it.

Berlie Doherty

The Cat and the Pig

Once, when I wasn't very big
I made a song about a pig
    Who ate a fig
    And wore a wig
And nimbly danced the Irish jig.

And when I was as small as THAT
I made a verse about a cat
    Who ate a rat
    And wore a hat
And sat (you've guessed) upon the mat.

And that, I thought, was that.

But yesterday upon my door
I heard a knock; I looked and saw
    A hatted cat
    A wiggèd pig
    Who chewed a rat
    Who danced the jig
    On my door mat!

They looked at me with faces wise
Out of their bright enquiring eyes,
"May we come in? For we are yours,
Pray do not leave us out of doors.
We are the children of your mind
Let us come in. Be kind. Be kind."

So now upon my fireside mat
There lies a tireless pussy cat
Who all day long chews on a rat
    And wears a hat.
And round him like a whirligig
Dancing a frantic Irish jig
Munching a fig, cavorts a big
    Wig-headed pig.

They eat my cakes and drink my tea.
There's hardly anything for me!
And yet I cannot throw them out
For they are mine without a doubt.

But when I'm at my desk tonight
I'll be more careful what I write.

I'll be more careful what I write.

Gerard Benson

Index of Authors